MEDICAL MALPRACTICE SERIES

MEDICAL MALPRACTICE

Handling Urology Cases

1991 Supplement
Current to August, 1991

William J. Morton, M.D., J.D.

Insert in the pocket at the back of the bound volume.

SHEPARD'S/McGRAW-HILL, INC.
P.O. Box 35300
Colorado Springs, Colorado 80935-3530

Copyright © 1991 by McGraw-Hill, Inc. All rights reserved. Printed in the United States of America. Except as permitted under the United States Copyright Act of 1976, no part of this publication may be reproduced or distributed in any form or by any means, or stored in a data base or retrieval system, without prior written permission of the publisher. Use of the program, documentation, and related materials is subject to the restrictions contained in the accompanying license agreement.

Information has been obtained by Shepard's/McGraw-Hill, Inc. from sources believed to be reliable. However, because of the possibility of human or mechanical error by our sources, Shepard's/McGraw-Hill, Inc., or others, Shepard's/McGraw-Hill, Inc. does not guarantee the accuracy, adequacy, or completeness of any information and is not responsible for any errors or omissions or for the results obtained from use of such information.

ISBN 0-07-172330-7

MMHUC1

When you are instructed to destroy this and other issues of Shepard's products, Shepard's/McGraw-Hill, Inc. respectfully requests that they be locally recycled to show your support and concern for saving and conserving our nation's natural resources. Thank you!

New sections and chapter appearing in this supplement

§1.40A National Practitioner Data Bank

§1.40B Emergency Medical Treatment and Active Labor Act (Anti-Dumping Act)

§1.49 Practice Parameters

§8.21 Laparoscopic Lymphadenectomy

Chapter 13 Examples of Urological Cases

§13.01 Failed Vasectomy

§13.02 Failure to Consult

§13.03 Reaction to Contrast Media

§13.04 Vasectomy Complications

§13.05 Vasectomy

§13.06 Delay in Diagnosing and Treating Testicular Cancer

§13.07 Failure to Diagnose Torsion of the Testicle

§13.08 Post-Operative Complications, Spoliation of Records

§13.09 Delayed Diagnosis of Prostate Cancer

§13.10 Unnecessary Penile Implant Surgery

§13.11 Infected Penile Prosthesis

§13.12 Urinary Incontinence after Transurethral Resection

About the Author

WILLIAM J. MORTON, M.D., J.D., is a diplomate of the American Board of Urology with more than 25 years of medical experience, now practicing adult and pediatric urology in Atlanta, Georgia. He is President of the American Board of Quality Assurance and Utilization Review Physicians and was the Medical Director of the Georgia Medical Care Foundation.

Dr. Morton is a graduate of the Woodrow Wilson College of Law, Atlanta, Secretary-General of the Urology Lawyers Council, and a member of the Georgia Bar, Association of Trial Lawyers of America, the Georgia Trial Lawyers Association, the National Health Lawyers Association, and the Lawyer-Pilots Bar Association.

1

Medical Malpractice Considerations

§1.23 Informed Consent

During an esophagogastroduodenoscopy and a dilation of a narrowed area of Steven Fore's esophagus, Dr. Charles Brown perforated the esophagus. At no time did Dr. Brown discuss the dilation procedure with Fore. Fore and his wife sued Dr. Brown, and the court granted Dr. Brown's motion for summary judgment on Fore's claim for lack of informed consent. Fore appealed, and the Alabama Supreme Court recognized questions of fact as to whether Fore would have consented to the dilation procedure, as well as to whether a reasonable person with Fore's characteristics would have consented to undergo the procedure with knowledge of the risks involved. The court reversed the lower court's grant of summary judgment and remanded the matter for trial. *Fore v Brown*, No CV-86-002494 (Ala Apr 1989).

Patricia Savold sued Dr. Dennis Johnson for malpractice, alleging that he performed surgery on her foot without obtaining her informed consent. The trial court granted defendant's motion for directed verdict on the grounds that Savold had failed to introduce expert testimony on the issue of informed consent. On appeal, the South Dakota Supreme Court reversed, noting that there was a factual dispute over whether Dr. Johnson provided Savold any information at all. If the jury believed that Savold was not provided with any information about the procedure, Savold would be relieved of the burden of proving, by expert testimony, that the doctor had failed to gain her informed consent. *Savold v Johnson*, No 16435-r-RAM (SD July 1989).

§1.25 Res Ipsa Loquitur

As a result of a subtotal thyroidectomy, Janice Poole suffered permanent bilateral vocal cord paralysis. Poole sued the University of Chicago, and the jury found for the defendant. On appeal, the Illinois Appellate Court concluded that plaintiff's evidence established that her bilateral vocal cord paralysis resulted from damage to her recurrent laryngeal nerves, but did not conclusively prove how or why the nerves were damaged. Consequently, the court reasoned that the trial court should have instructed the jury on the plaintiff's res ipsa loquitur claims. Thus, the appeals court reversed and remanded for the new trial. *Poole v University of Chicago*, 186 Ill App 3d 554, 542 NE2d 746 (1989).

§1.27 —Categories

Punitive Damages

The Georgia Supreme Court has upheld the constitutionality of Ga Code Ann §51-12-5.1(g)(1987), which provides for a $250,000 cap on the amount of punitive damages that may be awarded in a tort action. The court has also construed the statute to mean that $250,000 is the total amount of punitives that can be awarded in any case, no matter how many parties. *Bagley v Shortt*, No S91A0662 (Ga Sept 5, 1991).

§1.37 Release

The Supreme Court of Georgia, in *Posey v Medical Center-West, Inc*, addressed the issue of whether the release of one joint tortfeasor acts as a release of all joint tortfeasors. The court, after going through a lengthy discussion on the history of releases of joint tortfeasors, decided to overrule the long line of cases which held that a release of one joint tortfeasor acts as a release of all joint tortfeasors. The court went on to adopt the rule found in Restatement (Second) of Torts §885(1)(1979) which provides: "A valid release of one tortfeasor from liability for a harm given by the injured person does not discharge, others from the same harm, unless it is agreed that it will discharge them." *Posey v Medical Center-West, Inc*, 257 Ga 55, 354 SE2d 417 (1987).

§1.39 Peer Review

Dr. Harlan Stone sued the University of Maryland and others, alleging that he was forced to resign from his position as chief of the division of general surgery. After the university filed a motion for summary judgment, attaching as exhibits several medical committee review documents, the court entered an order, sealing the records with the exception of the complaint, amended complaint, and answers. The trial court found that Dr. Stone had resigned as part of an agreement to avoid facing disciplinary action, and granted summary judgment for the university.

Dr. Stone appealed and, while this appeal was pending, the Baltimore Sun Company was permitted to intervene to challenge the order sealing the records. The appeals court then affirmed the trial court's order, granting summary judgment on the merits, but overturned the trial court's order sealing the records, and remanded that part of the proceedings for further consideration. The trial court then lifted the seal on all information except for three peer review documents. The Sun appealed to the Fourth Circuit which certified to the Maryland Court of Appeals the issue of whether the state's law governing confidentiality of medical review committee materials bars press access to confidential records of a hospital's peer review committee when they are discoverable and have been filed with and considered by the court in connection with a dispositive motion such as a motion for summary judgment.

The Maryland Court of Appeals concluded "nothing in the statute even remotely suggests that once the committee records are properly subjected to pretrial discovery and may be admitted in evidence in the course of the civil action, that somehow, except as between the parties in the civil action, they remain insulated from public disclosure." Therefore, the court answered the certified question in the negative, saying peer review confidentiality does not bar press access to records which were introduced in doctors' staff privileges suit against the hospital. *Baltimore Sun Co v University of Md Medical System Corp*, 321 Md 659, 584 A2d 683 (1991).

§1.40A National Practitioner Data Bank (New)

The Health Care Quality Improvement Act of 1986, 42 USC §11101 *et seq* also established the National Practitioner Data Bank (NPDB or the Data Bank), an information clearing house to collect and release certain information related to the professional competence and conduct of physicians, dentists, and, in some cases, other health-care practitioners. This act is further described in 45 CFR pt 60 for the interested reader. Additionally, a guidebook to the NPDB for informational purposes is available from the United States Department of Health and Human Services, Health Resources and Services Administration, Parklawn Building, Rockville, Maryland.

There also is a toll-free telephone number for assistance regarding the Data Bank: 1-800-767-6732.

Basically, the NPDB is a central repository where information regarding any medical malpractice payment must be reported, as well as any disciplinary action related to professional competence or conduct. Hospitals, other health-care entities, state licensing boards, medical malpractice insurers, and professional societies all must abide by the regulatory processes of the act.

Unisys, a medical information systems corporation, was given the government contract to establish the data bank which became operational in October, 1990. While the early days of receiving and organizing the information have been vexing because of the massive amount of information received, eventually the flow of data will be more organized and categorized.

The NPDB had been criticized by physicians as being an unfair attack on their ability to discipline their own ranks, but in spite of this, the numbers of queries and reports to the Data Bank have been increasing. The information generally is not available to the public and, as a matter of fact, the only entity that can retrieve information from the Data Bank, other than the physician or health-care provider involved, is the hospital. It is mandatory for hospitals to query the Data Bank every two years when the physician applies for reappointment in order to satisfy the requirement of the statute. The only manner in which attorneys can get information from the Data Bank about individuals is if in a suit against a physician and a hospital, it can be determined that the hospital failed to query the Data Bank about that particular physician, then the plaintiff's attorney may be able to get information from the Data Bank about that particular defendant.

§1.40B Emergency Medical Treatment and Active Labor Act (Anti-Dumping Act)(New)

In 1985, Congress passed the Emergency Medical Treatment and Active Labor Act (Anti-Dumping Act) as part of the Consolidated Omnibus Budget Reconciliation Act of 1985, Pub L No 99-272, 100 Stat 82. This act required hospitals that received Medicare funds and which have an emergency room to make a determination and provide stabilizing treatment to women in active labor, as well as any "unstable" patient prior to transferring that patient. In 1989, Congress passed legislation which toughened these laws against "dumping" patients, and strengthened the scrutiny with which hospitals are being observed. As of this writing, only one physician has been fined, and this case, which went up to the Fifth Circuit Court of Appeals in July, 1991, has been finalized with both sides declining to appeal.

Dr. Michael Burditt was fined $20,000 for improperly transferring a woman in active labor to another hospital 160 miles away. The woman delivered a healthy baby one-half hour later on the side of the road. Dr. Burditt asserted that his reluctance to treat the patient arose from his fear of a malpractice suit arising from treating a high-risk patient who had not had proper prenatal care. However, the Fifth Circuit found that Dr. Burditt had knowingly violated the law and he was culpable because of his failure to "follow the advice of the nursing staff that the patient should not be transferred, failure to re-examine the patient before the transfer, and his refusal to treat her upon her return to his hospital." Thus, the court upheld the fine of $20,000. *Burditt v United States Department of Health & Human Services*, No 90-4511 (5th Cir July 9, 1991).

Other cases have arisen regarding the attempt to use the Emergency Medical Treatment and Active Labor Act in medical malpractice actions, but generally have been unsuccessful. An example is the case involving Alice Gatewood who sued the Washington Hospital Center, asserting a claim under the *act* when her husband died of a heart attack one day after he was discharged from the Washington Hospital Center Emergency Room. The trial court dismissed the case on the grounds that the *act* did not apply to fully insured patients who were misdiagnosed in an emergency room. The Federal Appeals Court held that a patient's insurance status was irrelevant to a claim under the act, but that the act was "not intended to create a broad federal cause of action for Emergency Room negligence or malpractice." The appeals court affirmed the trial court's dismissal of the complaint for failure to state a claim upon which relief could be granted. *Gatewood v Washington Healthcare Corp*, No 90-7094 (DC Cir May 28, 1991).

However, an Illinois court refused to dismiss a case based upon the Emergency Medical Treatment Act, wherein plaintiff Michelle Thompson brought an action, alleging that defendant doctors and hospitals failed to provide her with proper medical treatment in connection with the premature delivery of her baby. Her claim is that, on the morning of April 8, 1988, she presented herself at the emergency room of St. Anne's Hospital in Chicago. At that time, she was, according to Thompson, inappropriately transferred to defendant Cook County Hospital where she arrived at 3:30 that same morning. Thompson claimed that Cook County Hospital's personnel also failed to properly examine her, monitor her, or stabilize her and, thus, she went into active labor about an hour after arriving at Cook County Hospital. The premature infant survived only five hours.

Based on these allegations, plaintiff brought suit, claiming violations of the Emergency Medical Treatment and Active Labor Act. The hospitals filed a Motion to Dismiss, contending that they did not engage in patient dumping. The court refused to grant defendants' motion, finding that Thompson had stated a claim that defendants violated the section of the law which prohibits the denial of stabilizing treatment to patients having an emergency medical condition or in labor. *Thompson v St Anne's Hospital*, 716 F Supp 8 (ND Ill July 1989).

§1.42 —Collateral Source

While numerous jurisdictions are striking down or upholding various parts of the tort reform movement, a recent case in Georgia declared unconstitutional the Georgia Code which allows the admission of evidence of collateral source benefits in civil actions. The court decided the statute violated Ga Const 1983, art 1, §1, ¶2 which states that: "Protection to person and property is the paramount duty of government and shall be impartial and complete. No person shall be denied the equal protection of the laws." Georgia Code Ann §51-12-1(B) (Michie 1987) violated that constitutional provision, as it allowed juries to consider inherently prejudicial evidence which could defeat a plaintiff's statutory right to recover damages resulting from another tortious act. The court also found that the statute violated the state constitution's due process clause, as it did not suggest what juries should do with evidence of payments from collateral sources. *Denton v Con-Way Express, Inc*, No S90A1101 (Apr 4, 1991).

§1.44 —Limitation of Awards

Helen and Roger Boyd sued Dr. Bulala for medical malpractice, alleging negligence in delivering their now-deceased daughter Veronica. A jury awarded Veronica $1.8 million in compensatory damages and $1 million in punitive damages. Helen Boyd was awarded $1.5 million in compensatory damages and $1 million in punitive damages, and Roger Boyd was awarded $1.1 million in compensatory damages. The Boyds were also awarded $1.7 million for Veronica's medical expenses. The trial court entered the judgment, holding that Virginia's cap on medical malpractice awards violated the federal constitutional right to a jury trial. The defendant appealed, and the Fourth Circuit Court of Appeals noted that the Virginia Supreme Court had held that the malpractice cap was constitutional under both the federal Constitution and the state constitution. The court deferred to the Virginia Supreme Court's interpretation of the state constitution and agreed that the cap did not violate the federal Constitution. In so ruling, the court rejected the plaintiff's arguments that the cap violated: (1) their right to a jury trial; (2) the separation of powers; and (3) due process and equal protection. The court thus upheld Virginia's medical malpractice cap. *Boyd v Bulala*, 877 F2d 1191 (4th Cir 1989).

§1.49 Practice Parameters (New)

Practice parameters are strategies for patient management developed to assist physicians in clinical decision-making and identify a range of diagnostic or therapeutic management of specific clinical conditions or specific interventions which may be appropriate. Practice parameters include guidelines, standards, and other patient-management strategies. Thirty-two physician organizations in the United States have developed over 1,100 practice parameters. Just a few examples of practice parameters follow:

1. The management of patients with acute myocardial infarction developed by the American College of Cardiology provides early management recommendations. The guidelines address detection, including laboratory criteria and assessment of ventricular performance, as well as management of acute infarction.
2. Retinal detachment is another practice parameter developed by the American Academy of Ophthalmology. Additionally, the American Academy of Ophthalmology has developed practice parameters for glaucoma, diabetic retinopathy, and macular degeneration, and other conditions.
3. The American College of Obstetrics and Gynecology has also developed practice parameters for performing gynecological intra-abdominal laser therapy, treatment of cancer of the ovary, and the diagnosis and management of postpartum hemorrhage.
4. The American Urological Association is developing practice parameters on transurethral resection of the prostate.

Obviously, there are literally hundreds of other practice parameters which have been developed by medical specialties, and some of the publications that address this include: American Medical Assn, Office of Quality Assurance, *Practice Parameters Update* (1990); American Medical Assn, *1990 Directory of Practice Parameters* (1990) which cites 1,000 practice parameters developed by medical specialty organizations and American Medical Assn, *Legal Implications of Practice Parameters*.

Interestingly, some practice parameters become obsolete, and one should write to each specialty society to determine current practice parameters. As of this writing, the American College of Obstetrics and Gynecology has withdrawn (but replaced) information on management of isoimmunization in pregnancy, laser technology, and the adolescent obstetric gynecologic patient.

2

Opening the File

§2.19 Affirmative Defenses

Dominique Smith was allegedly negligently injured during his birth at a United States Army Hospital in Italy. The Smiths filed suit against Dr. Marshall, but the court granted the government's motion to substitute itself for Dr. Marshall pursuant to the Gonzalez Act which provides that in a suit against military medical personnel for employment-related torts, the government is to be substituted as the defendant and the suit is to proceed under the Federal Tort Claims Act, ch 753, 60 Stat 812, tit 4 (FTCA). The court then dismissed the suit on the grounds that the FTCA excludes recovery for injuries sustained abroad. The Ninth United States Circuit Court of Appeals reversed, holding that neither the Gonzalez Act nor the Federal Employees Liability Reform and Tort Compensation Act of 1988, Pub L No 100-694, 102 Stat 4563 required substitution of the government or otherwise immunized Dr. Marshall. It ruled that the act confers absolute immunity on government employees by making an FTCA action against the government the exclusive remedy for their employment-related torts. *United States v Smith*, No 89-1646 (9th Cir Mar 20, 1991).

However, consider the following: Dean Lilly sued Dr. Paul Fieldstone for malpractice, alleging that while Lilly was a patient at the Erwin Army Hospital, Dr. Fieldstone treated him negligently. The Federal District Court substituted the United States for Dr. Fieldstone, holding that he was an employee of the government. Lilly appealed, and the Tenth Circuit concluded that Dr. Fieldstone was, in fact, an independent contractor over whom the United States exercised little control. The appeals court reversed the trial court's order, and remanded the case for further proceedings. *Lilly v Fieldstone*, 876 F2d 857 (10th Cir 1989).

3

Medical Records

§3.23 Abbreviations

ASA	aspirin
ASAP	as soon as possible
EMUL	emulsion
Fe	iron
LOC	laxative of choice
mEq	milliequivalent
MOM	milk of magnesia
NKDA	no known drug allergies
NS	normal saline
NTG	nitroglycerin
OINT	ointment
PCA	patient controlled analgesia
PIT	pitocin
SUBQ	subcutaneously
SUPP	suppository
TLOA	temporary leave of absence
TPA	tissue plasmin activator
TPN	total parenteral nutrition

4

Urology as a Specialty

§4.04 Licensure

Results of the first National Board of Medical Examiners test ever administered to foreign medical graduates (FMGs) have not borne out some FMGs' claims that their separate licensure examination process has been discriminating against them. FMGs scored an average of 14 points lower on the National Boards Part I and Part II than on the Foreign Medical Graduate Examination in the Medical Sciences, their equivalent of the National Boards. Faced with past passing rates of more than 80 per cent for United States medical students on the National Boards compared with less than 33 per cent for FMGs taking the Educational Council for Foreign Medical Graduates Exam, many FMGs have been assuming that their examination is a more difficult one than the National Boards. However, the results showed that FMGs scored a 16 per cent pass rate on the National Boards Part I, compared with a 30 per cent pass rate for FMGs taking the first part of the Educational Council for Foreign Medical Graduates Exam.

As expected, alien FMGs did significantly better on the National Boards than did United States citizens who had graduated from foreign medical schools: 19.6 per cent of alien FMGs passed Part I, compared with 9.6 per cent of United States citizens who were graduates of foreign medical schools.

§4.10 Urological Societies

The American Urological Association has issued its latest membership roster which reveals that total membership includes 7,476 urologists divided into nine categories from active (4,914) to resident (337) to honorary (44), and others.

6

The Use of Instruments and Devices in Diagnosis, Evaluation, and Treatment of the Urogenital Tract

§6.02 Urethral Catheters

A two-year-old child underwent a retrograde cystogram, employing the use of a Foley catheter. The balloon on the catheter was not able to deflate, and attempts to remove the balloon were unsuccessful. Two ccs of ether were inserted by a blunt needle down the tube, resulting in the immediate rupture of the balloon. Plaintiff brought an action against the manufacturer of the catheter, alleging that it was defectively designed, and the defendant argued that the catheter adhered to the industry standard. Because the plaintiff initially suffered from hemorrhagic cystitis, probably chemical in origin, for months with decreasing intensity, it was alleged that the child would require five to six years of therapy during her adolescent years to correct or avoid a sexual dysfunction. There was a jury verdict award to the plaintiff of $150,000. *Evans v CR Bard, Inc*, No 87-2-00447-2 (Yakima County Super Ct, Wash June 10, 1988).

7

Radiology of the Urinary Tract

§7.02 Excretory Urography

The introduction of low-osmolar contrast agents (LOCA) has greatly reduced the number of allergic reactions to patients undergoing radiologic procedures which involve injection of contrast media. These new agents are proven to be much safer than the conventional high-osmolar contrast media currently in use, but are approximately 12 to 15 times higher in cost.

Thus, urologists (and others) are faced with the decision of using an extremely expensive method of diagnostic modality versus one that has a higher risk of untoward results (possibly even death), but at a much lower cost. The benefit versus risk argument surfaces again. While nothing substitutes for an excellent history regarding allergies in the patient, by not using the expensive low-osmolar contract agent in the face of an unsuspected but deadly allergic reaction to the conventional high-osmolar contrast agent will certainly spawn more lawsuits.

8

Common Urological Surgical Procedures

§8.21 Laparoscopic Lymphadenectomy (New)

For the last 50 years, laparoscopy has been largely the province of the gynecologist. In urology, the laparoscope has now been used to perform pelvic lymph node dissection prior to planned therapy for localized prostate cancer. Indeed, the learning curve on the use of the laparoscope by urologists to perform this somewhat noninvasive surgery is great, but will certainly save the patient significant pain, suffering, and expense if properly performed.

I am aware of at least one instance where the aorta was lacerated during the insertion of the trocar prior to ever performing the laparoscopic lymph node dissection, but this injury was recognized immediately, vascular surgery consult was obtained, and the patient survived the episode with very little damage. As of this writing, I am unaware that a lawsuit has been filed in this instance.

9

Common Urological Complications

§9.07 Allergic or Toxic Drug Reactions

Plaintiff's decedent was being treated for obesity and high blood pressure and, based upon the decedent's complaints and without performing a urinalysis, a diagnosis of chronic urinary tract infection was made and Macrodantin prescribed. This prescription was continued over the telephone without further urinalysis for the subsequent four years. In August, 1986, liver function tests performed on the decedent suggested fatty infiltrates in the liver. A subsequent biopsy revealed cirrhosis of the liver, and the patient succumbed at age 57 in October, 1987. Based upon the continued use of Macrodantin, despite a warning in the *Physician's Desk Reference* that use of Macrodantin for long periods of time poses a risk of liver damage, a $1 million settlement was reached. *Staton v Pivinick*, No 89-6041-M (Dallas County Dist Ct, Tex (1989)).

12

Evolution of Hospital Liability

§12.03 —Charitable Immunity

A recent case in Georgia has been heard by the court of appeals and expanded somewhat the charitable immunity of physicians for their conduct. The ruling came in two medical malpractice cases filed against the Hospital Authority of Fulton County and, in both cases, the Hospital Authority's motion for summary judgment on the basis of governmental immunity was denied, the Hospital Authority appealed, and the court of appeals reversed.

The court of appeals ruled that the Hospital Authority and any entity created pursuant to the Hospital Authority's law, Ga Code Ann §31-7-71 *et seq* (1974), is a county entity entitled to assert the defense of governmental immunity in civil suits despite the existence of a self-insurance fund set up by the Hospital Authority. *Hospital Authority v Litterilla*, No A90A1553 (Ga Ct App Mar 8, 1991); *Hospital Authority v Hyde*, No A90A1814 (Ga Ct App Mar 8, 1991).

§12.08 —Borrowed Servant

As a follow-up of the *Ross v Chatham County Hospital Authority* case, where the court reversed summary judgment for the hospital concluding that there were factual issues to be resolved, on remand, the trial court entered summary judgment in favor of the hospital on the entire complaint, holding there were no other negligent acts that could be considered administrative. Ross appealed, challenging the trial court's initial grant of partial summary judgment, based on the locality rule. The appeals court reversed, initially ruling that appellate review was not precluded by Ross' earlier failure to file a cross appeal. The court ruled that the locality rule was inapplicable because the ability of operating personnel to count instruments does not depend on the size or location of the hospital. Thus, as Ross presented expert testimony that the failure to count instruments violated the standard of care, summary judgment was inappropriate. *Ross v Chatham County Hospital Authority*, No A91 A0375 (Ga Ct App July 12, 1991).

§12.10 Expert Witness

Plaintiff Vakil filed a pro se medical malpractice action against the Mayo Clinic and St. Mary's Hospital. She contended that those facilities had rendered improper treatment for a neck and shoulder injury she sustained in an automobile accident. The district court dismissed her claim due to her failure to file an affidavit of expert review, as required by state statute. Plaintiff appealed, and the Eighth Circuit ruled that the expert review statute applied only if there was a finding that expert testimony was necessary to establish a prima facie case of malpractice. Since the lower court had made no such findings in the matter, the appellate court reversed and remanded the matter to the district court for determination of this issue. *Vakil v Mayo Clinic*, 878 F2d 238 (8th Cir 1989).

§12.13 Corporate Practice of Medicine

Morton Canton admitted plaintiff's 68-year-old wife to a hospital in North Miami. At the time, Canton, masquerading as a medical doctor under the name of Dr. Michelle LaBella, a dead Italian doctor, was on the staff of Biscayne Hospital. Plaintiff's decedent died 18 days after admission, and it was later learned that Canton was not a medical doctor, but was a fugitive from Canada who Florida had unsuspectingly licensed as a physician under a false name. The husband filed a wrongful death action against the hospital, contending that the hospital was negligent in screening out and verifying Canton's credentials and for granting him staff privileges.

The Federal District Court directed a verdict for the defendant hospital on the ground that the hospital was not vicariously liable for the tortious acts of an independent contractor physician. On plaintiff's appeal to the Eleventh Circuit, that court certified to Florida's Supreme Court the crucial question: "Whether . . . hospitals owed a duty to their patients to select and retain competent physicians who, although they are independent practitioners, would be providing in-house patient care through their hospital staff privileges." The Florida Supreme Court, in a unanimous decision, held that hospitals are liable for any negligence in selecting, retaining, and granting staff privileges to incompetent independent doctors. *Insinga v LaBella*, 543 So 2d 209 (Fla 1989).

In another case exemplifying vicarious liability with negligent credentialing, the Pitt County Memorial Hospital is a teaching hospital for the East Carolina University Medical School. The medical school, in turn, contracted with Eastern OB/GYN Associates for supervision of the residents. In December, 1984, Sandra Mozingo was admitted to the hospital to deliver her second child and during the delivery, the child's shoulder became wedged. The resident physicians attending Mozingo called Dr. Kazior from the Eastern OB/GYN Associates for assistance. Although Dr. Kazior came immediately to the hospital, the delivery had been completed by the time he arrived and the child was born with many disabilities, allegedly resulting from the severe shoulder dystocia. The Mozingos then sued Dr. Kazior, as well as the hospital and the chief resident. The trial court granted summary judgment for Dr. Kazior but on appeal, the court found that Dr. Kazior had "undertaken a responsibility as an employee of Eastern to render supervisory medical services to the Medical School's residency program, and thereby to the residents training under it and, at least indirectly, to the patients under the residents' care." The court found that summary judgment was not appropriate on the issue of whether Dr. Kazior owed a duty to the child arising from the contractual relationship between Eastern and the medical school. *Mozingo v Pitt County Memorial Hospital*, 101 NC App 578, 400 SE2d 747 (1991).

13

Examples of Urological Cases (New)

§13.01 Failed Vasectomy

In this medical malpractice action, plaintiffs claimed that the defendant negligently performed a vasectomy and failed to conduct and interpret post-operative tests. As a proximate result of this negligence, Mrs. Owens delivered a child who was diagnosed as having Down's Syndrome. In addition to expenses related to the pregnancy and delivery of the child, the plaintiffs sought damages for the extraordinary costs which will be incurred as a result of the birth of a handicapped child. Defendant filed a motion to dismiss the plaintiffs' claim for emotional injuries, and the trial court granted this motion. The appellate court certified the following questions to the Supreme Court: (1) When a health-care provider in Tennessee breaches a duty to impart information or to perform medical procedures with due care resulting in the birth of a handicapped child, does this breach give rise to an action for wrongful birth? (2) When it has been shown that a health-care provider has breached a duty to impart information or to perform medical procedures with due care, resulting in the birth of a defective or handicapped child, are the emotional injuries to the parents and the extraordinary expenses attributable to the birth defect compensable elements of damage?

The Supreme Court found that the record in this case was too scanty to resolve these issues. However, it held that "[i]f it can be established by appropriate pleadings and probative evidence that acts or omissions of a defendant are the proximate cause of injuries sustained by a plaintiff, he is entitled to recover." The Supreme Court said the trial court should allow plaintiffs to amend their complaint to allege that the child's injuries resulted from the negligence of the physician. If they can prove their claim, the

Supreme Court said plaintiffs should be able to recover damages, including those for emotional distress. *Owens v Foote*, 773 SW2d 911 (Tenn 1989).

§13.02   Failure to Consult

After two unsuccessful urological procedures, the patient underwent a left ureteral reimplantation performed by Dr. Simmons and others. During this procedure, the left external iliac artery and vein were severed. Without vascular consult, the urologists attempted repair, but in the recovery room, the leg was noted to be blue and without detectable pulses. At that time, a vascular surgeon was consulted, and the patient underwent an iliofemoral bypass which resulted in a subsequent amputation of the patient's leg and eventual kidney failure from which he died.

The suit alleged that when the urologists discovered the dense scarring and adhesions in the retroperitoneal cavity, they should have considered alternative surgical techniques and called for an immediate vascular consult in the operating room. A settlement was reached for $430,000. *Watt v Simmons*, No 85-416-CA01 (Sarasota County Cir Ct, Fla July 1986).

§13.03   Reaction to Contrast Media

In December, 1986, a 23-year-old woman underwent an intravenous pyelogram test and immediately incurred an anaphylactoid reaction to the dye. She succumbed the next day. An action was brought against the medical clinic and physician, alleging that the defendants were negligent in injecting the patient with the dye while she was in a state of extreme anxiety, failing to be prepared for an emergency resulting from an anaphylactoid reaction, and failing to warn of the dangers of the procedure. A jury verdict of $1.6 million was made to the plaintiff, and the case is currently on appeal. *Rivera v M&S X-Ray Associates, PA*, No 87-CI-21488 (Bexar County Dist Ct, Tex Feb 1989).

§13.04   Vasectomy Complications

Jerry Vickers had a vasectomy performed by Dr. Witt. A few days later, Vickers saw Dr. Austin for medical care and treatment. Over the next several months, Dr. Austin removed Vickers' right and left testicles because of pain.

Vickers originally sued Dr. Witt only, but Dr. Witt impleaded Dr. Austin as a third-party defendant, after which Vickers amended his complaint to include Dr. Austin. Before trial, Dr. Witt negotiated a settlement with Vickers for $140,000 and then asked Dr. Austin to contribute to this settlement, but Dr. Austin refused. Dr. Witt paid Vickers $140,000 and dismissed the cross-claim against Dr. Austin, and then sued to recover from Dr. Austin the amount he paid to settle the previous lawsuit. Dr. Austin objected to Dr. Witt's complaint on the ground that it failed to allege that Dr. Witt was negligent in his treatment of Vickers. Dr. Witt argued that the only issue was Dr. Austin's negligence, and that Dr. Witt's negligence, if any, had become irrelevant. A jury found for Dr. Witt, but the trial court granted Dr. Austin a new trial. On appeal, the court affirmed the grant of a new trial, finding that Dr. Witt, as the initial tortfeasor, and Dr. Austin, as the successor tortfeasor, each bore the expense of his own fault. The court noted that the evidence was sufficient for a jury to find that Dr. Witt negligently failed to ensure a sterile field for the vasectomy, the negligence produced an infection, the infection produced scarring, and the scarring required removal of the right testicle. The jury also could have concluded that Vickers' experience with the right-sided testicle "preprocessed" him for pain on the left side. *Witt v Austin*, No WD432677 (Mo Ct App Feb 1991).

§13.05 Vasectomy

Swaw underwent bilateral vasectomy performed by Dr. Klompien. The next day when Swaw called complaining of swelling and discoloration between the umbilicus and the rectum, he was told by Dr. Klompien's partner to apply ice. The following day, Swaw called Dr. Klompien who recommended heat. Swaw went in to see the physician two days later, but the wound was not drained. Swaw suffered pain and discomfort with sex which was almost relieved by removal of fibrotic tissue during a repeat vasectomy. The suit alleged inadequate post-operative care, and the jury awarded $510,000 to Swaw. *Swaw v Klompien*, No 84M5-756 (Cook County Cir Ct, Ill Oct 1986).

§13.06 Delay in Diagnosing and Treating Testicular Cancer

In February, 1987, the plaintiff consulted a general physician regarding severe swelling of his right testicle. The physician considered the possibility of a tumor, but diagnosed an inflammation and placed the patient on antibiotic therapy. When this failed to resolve the swelling, the patient was referred to a urologist who performed exploratory surgery, pulled the testicle up into the wound, visualized and palpated it, and then returned the testicle to the patient's scrotum. The doctor's post-operative diagnosis was "inflammatory process." Three or four weeks later, the plaintiff returned complaining that the testicle was swelling and, at that time, was referred to a second urologist.

On March 30, 1987, the second urologist did an orchiectomy, the pathology report of which indicated seminoma. A lawsuit was brought against the first urologist, alleging that he fell below the standard of care when he performed exploratory surgery and failed to do any type of biopsy. The defendant argued that his diagnosis and treatment were within the standard of care. A jury verdict resulted in $136,000 for the plaintiff. *Nastasi v Johnson*, No N38713 (Vista County Super Ct, Cal 1989).

§13.07 Failure to Diagnose Torsion of the Testicle

On February 14, 1985, a 22-year-old patient awoke with severe pain in the right testicle and was seen in the emergency room of a hospital where a physician diagnosed his condition as epididymitis. Two days later, the patient returned to the hospital, complaining that the pain and swelling had worsened, and was treated by the same doctor who had seen him originally. The doctor continued to diagnose the condition as epididymitis and prescribed another antibiotic. Two days later, the patient returned to the emergency room again where a different physician referred the patient to a urologist who diagnosed the condition as torsion and performed an orchiectomy that same day.

The plaintiff brought an action against the first physician in the hospital, alleging negligent failure to diagnose torsion of the testicle and failure to refer to a urologist. The defendants argued that epididymitis was the correct diagnosis. A urinalysis performed at the hospital indicated the presence of white blood cells, and the clinical examination did not reveal the classic symptoms of torsion. The defendants further argued that, even if the diagnosis was incorrect, the testicle most likely would have been lost anyway because more than four hours elapsed between the onset of the symptoms and the first examination. The jury verdict was returned on behalf of the plaintiff for $106,000. *Cowles v Browne*, No SM50577 (Santa Barbara County Super Ct, Cal Dec 1988).

§13.08 Post-Operative Complications, Spoliation of Records

A patient, at age three, had reflux of urine into both ureters, and underwent a bilateral ureteral reimplantation. Excessive scar tissue formed, blocking one ureter partially and the other totally, but the obstructions went undiscovered for seven months, causing a 70 per cent loss of kidney function. The suit was filed, alleging that the physician was negligent for operating while the plaintiff was infected and for failing to take x-rays post-operatively to determine the success of the operation. When review of the physicians notes at the patient's three-month post-operative check-up was performed, the records reflected "No complaints." Counsel became suspicious and consulted a documents expert who confirmed that the records had been altered. When confronted by this, the defendant admitted that he had doctored the entry, and the plaintiff then moved to amend the petition to add a claim for punitive damages. The parties agreed to a structured settlement with the present value of $1.4 million. *Rinehart v Albani*, No CV84-1677 (Clay County Dist Ct, Mo Oct 1986).

§13.09 Delayed Diagnosis of Prostate Cancer

The patient consulted urologist Scott who performed a transurethral resection (TUR) of the prostate and a subsequent radical prostatectomy when the pathology report revealed prostate cancer. During the radical prostatectomy, the rectum was perforated. The suit was brought against urologist Scott, alleging that he had: (1) failed to perform appropriate tests to diagnose the prostate cancer earlier; (2) performed unnecessary surgery by completing the TUR given the positive biopsy results; and (3) failed to treat the rectal perforation to prevent formation of the rectourethral fistula.

The jury awarded $855,000 to the plaintiff, but noneconomic damages were reduced to $250,000 pursuant to California's damages cap. *Funk v Scott*, No 632431-9 (Alameda County Super Ct, Cal May 1989).

§13.10 Unnecessary Penile Implant Surgery

Patient Tenkin consulted three different urologists for his diagnosis of Peyronie's disease. Each of these physicians told him not to undergo corrective treatment. The patient then called Dr. Bush, a Chicago urologist, who agreed to do an examination while he was passing through New Jersey. The parties met in a restaurant, and Dr. Bush conducted a cursory examination in the men's room. He then persuaded Tenkin to undergo implantation of prosthetic rods into the penis. The patient's wife opposed the surgery because her husband had had a stroke and, indeed, when the patient suffered another stroke, the surgery was delayed for an additional two years.

Dr. Bush neglected to reexamine the patient prior to then performing the implant, and Tenkin developed a post-operative infection where he was sent home to New Jersey and treated by Dr. Bush over the telephone. Gangrene had developed on the patient's penis, and the rods had to be removed. Tenkin brought suit against Dr. Bush, alleging lack of informed consent for the surgery and intra- and post-operative negligence. The jury awarded $912,000 to the plaintiff, but reduced the award by 25 per cent after finding Tenkin contributorily negligent for not heeding the advice of other urologists to forego the surgery. *Tenkin v Bush*, No L-085860M M (Sussex County Super Ct, NJ Aug 1967).

§13.11   Infected Penile Prosthesis

The plaintiff, a paraplegic, underwent an implantation of an inflatable penile prosthesis with detachable rear-tip extenders. Within a month, he developed an infection, and the prosthesis eroded through the tip of the penis. Two weeks later, the prosthesis was surgically removed, but the resident physician forgot to remove the rear-tip extenders which had become detached. Three months later, the defendant hospital realized the error and successfully performed a second surgery to remove the extenders, but the delay reduced the plaintiff's capacity to successfully undergo another implantation to approximately 20 per cent. Plaintiff contended that had the prosthesis been completely removed in the first surgery, he would have been willing to undergo another reimplantation. The jury awarded $250,000, and the plaintiff agreed to a $175,000 post-trial settlement in lieu of appeal. *Ault v St Louis University Medical Center*, No 822-00869 (St Louis County Cir Ct, Mo Mar 1986).

§13.12   Urinary Incontinence after Transurethral Resection

Patient Poss sued his urologist, Dr. Roper, claiming permanent urinary incontinence after a transurethral resection (TUR). He also asserted that he only gave Roper permission to do a cystoscopy and biopsy of the prostate and not a surgical procedure such as TUR. Roper introduced into evidence a form signed by Poss consenting to a TUR. In addition, a videotape had been made, showing a surgical laceration of the sphincter, but the defendant's witness disagreed, saying the laceration was actually a well-known anatomical landmark and not evidence of a slip of the knife. In addition, a recent test revealed that Poss had a neurological impairment which caused his bladder to be inelastic; since it did not expand, urine was pushed out as the bladder filled up. The trial resulted in a defense verdict. *Poss v Roper*, No 86-11399-6 (July 1991).

Sam Hawkins underwent a routine transurethral resection (TUR) by Dr. Nicholas Bath in 1988 and was immediately incontinent subsequent to the catheter removal in the hospital. He filed an action for damages against Dr. Bath whose defense was that because the operation was very bloody (an event not noted in the operative note, progress note, or discharge summary, but in an affidavit filed separately some two years after the lawsuit was instituted), he did indeed cut the sphincter causing incontinence, but this was a "known risk" of the procedure and not negligence.

At trial, plaintiff showed the elements of doing a proper TUR were: (1) know the anatomy; (2) know where the end of the "cutting" loop is when one is "cutting"; and (3) do not cut when you cannot see. A jury verdict was rendered for the plaintiff in the amount of $125,000. *Hawkins v Bath*, No 90-3323-4 (DeKalb County Super Ct, Ga Aug 1991).

Cases

A

Ault v St Louis Univ Medical Center, No 822-00869 (St Louis County Cir Ct, Mo Mar 1986) §13.11

B

Bagley v Shortt, No S91A0662 (Ga Sept 5, 1991) §1.27

Baltimore Sun Co v University of Md Medical Sys Corp, 321 Md 659, 584 A2d 683 (1991) §1.39

Boyd v Bulala, 877 F2d 1191 (4th Cir 1989) §1.44

Burditt v United States Dept of Health & Human Servs, No 90-4511 (5th Cir July 9, 1991) §1.40B

C

Cowles v Browne, No SM50577 (Santa Barbara County Super Ct, Cal Dec 1988) §13.07

D

Denton v Con-Way Express, Inc, No S90A1101 (Apr 4, 1991) §1.42

E

Evans v CR Bard, Inc, No 87-2-00447-2 (Yakima County Super Ct, Wash June 10, 1988) §6.02

F

Fore v Brown, No CV-86-002494 (Ala Apr 1989) §1.23

Funk v Scott, No 632431-9 (Alameda County Super Ct, Cal May 1989) §13.09

G

Gatewood v Washington
  Healthcare Corp, No 90-7094
  (DC Cir May 28, 1991)
  §1.40B

H

Hawkins v Bath, No 90-3323-4
  (DeKalb County Super Ct,
  Ga Aug 1991) **§13.12**
Hospital Auth v Hyde, No
  A90A1814 (Ga Ct App
  Mar 8, 1991) **§12.03**
Hospital Auth v Litterilla, No
  A90A1553 (Ga Ct App
  Mar 8, 1991) **§12.03**

I

Insinga v LaBella, 543 So 2d
  209 (Fla 1989) **§12.13**

L

Lilly v Fieldstone, 876 F2d 857
  (10th Cir 1989) **§2.19**

M

Mozingo v Pitt County
  Memorial Hosp, 101 NC App
  578, 400 SE2d 747 (1991)
  §12.13

N

Nastasi v Johnson, No N38713
  (Vista County Super Ct, Cal
  1989) **§13.06**

O

Owens v Foote, 773 SW2d 911
  (Tenn 1989) **§13.01**

P

Poole v University of Chicago,
  186 Ill App 3d 554, 542
  NE2d 746 (1989) **§1.25**
Posey v Medical Center-West,
  Inc, 257 Ga 55, 354 SE2d
  417 (1987) **§1.37**
Poss v Roper, No 86-11399-6
  (July 1991) **§13.12**

R

Rinehart v Albani, No
  CV84-1677 (Clay County
  Dist Ct, Mo Oct 1986)
  §13.08
Rivera v M&S X-Ray Assocs,
  PA, No 87-CI-21488 (Bexar
  County Dist Ct, Tex Feb
  1989) **§13.03**
Ross v Chatham County Hosp
  Auth, No A91 A0375
  (July 12, 1991) **§12.08**

S

Savold v Johnson, No
  16435-r-Ram (SD July 1989)
  §1.23

Staton v Pivinick, No
 89-6041-M (Dallas County
 Dist Ct, Tex 1989) §**9.07**
Swaw v Klompien, No
 84M5-756 (Cook County Cir
 Ct, Ill Oct 1986) §**13.05**

T

Tenkin v Bush, No L-085860M
 M (Sussex County Super Ct,
 NJ Aug 1967) §**13.10**
Thompson v St Anne's Hosp,
 716 F Supp 8 (ND Ill 1989)
 §**1.40B**

U

United States v Smith, No
 89-1646 (9th Cir Mar 20,
 1991) §**2.19**

V

Vakil v Mayo Clinic, 878 F2d
 238 (8th Cir 1989) §**12.10**

W

Watt v Simmons, No
 85-416-CA01 (July 1986)
 §**13.02**
Witt v Austin, No WD432677
 (Mo Ct App Feb 1991)
 §**13.04**

Statutes

United States Code

42 USC §11101 et seq **§1.40A**

State Statutes

Ga Code Ann §31-7-71 et seq
 §12.03
Ga Code Ann §51-12-1(B)
 §1.42
Ga Code Ann §51-12-5.1(g)
 §1.27

Authorities

A

American Medical Assn, Legal Implications of Practice Parameters (1990) §1.49

American Medical Assn, Office of Quality Assurance, Practice Parameters Update (1990) §1.49

American Medical Assn, 1990 Directory of Practice Parameters §1.49

R

Restatement (Second) of Torts (1979) §1.37

Index

A

ANTI-DUMPING ACT
  See EMERGENCY MEDICAL TREATMENT AND ACTIVE LABOR ACT

C

CANCER
  Prostate cancer. See PROSTATE CANCER
  Testicular cancer. See TESTICULAR CANCER
CONSOLIDATED OMNIBUS BUDGET RECONCILIATION ACT (COBRA)
  Malpractice considerations §1.40B
CONTRAST MEDIA, REACTION TO
  Urological cases, examples of §13.03

D

DATA BANK
  See NATIONAL PRACTITIONER DATA BANK (NPDB)

E

EMERGENCY MEDICAL TREATMENT AND ACTIVE LABOR ACT
  Malpractice considerations §1.40B

M

MALPRACTICE CONSIDERATIONS
  Emergency Medical Treatment and Active Labor Act §1.40B
  National Practitioner Data Bank (NPDB) §1.40A
  Practice parameters §1.49

N

NATIONAL PRACTITIONER DATA BANK (NPDB)
  Malpractice considerations §1.40A

P

PENILE-IMPLANT SURGERY
Urological cases, examples of §13.10

PENILE PROSTHESIS, INFECTED
Urological cases, examples of §13.11

POST-OPERATIVE COMPLICATIONS
Urological cases, examples of §13.08

PRACTICE PARAMETERS
Malpractice considerations §1.49

PROSTATE CANCER
Urological cases, examples of §13.09

T

TESTICLE, TORSION OF
Urological cases, examples of §13.07

TESTICULAR CANCER
Urological cases, examples of §13.06

TRANSURETHRAL RESECTION (TUR), INCONTINENCE AFTER
Urological cases, examples of §13.12

U

UROLOGICAL CASES, EXAMPLES OF
Contrast media, reaction to §13.03
Failed vasectomy §13.01
Failure to consult §13.02
Incontinence after TUR §13.12
Infected penile prosthesis §13.11
Penile implant surgery §13.10
Post-operative complications §13.08
Prostate cancer §13.09
Testicular cancer §13.06
Torsion of testicle §13.07
Vasectomy §13.05
Vasectomy complications §13.04

V

VASECTOMY
Urological cases, examples of §§13.01-13.05